Specials!

Industrial Britain
1750–1900

Nichola Boughey

Acknowledgements

© 2006 Folens Limited, on behalf of the author.

United Kingdom: Folens Publishers, Apex Business Centre, Boscombe Road, Dunstable, LU5 4RL.
Email: folens@folens.com

Ireland: Folens Publishers, Greenhills Road, Tallaght, Dublin 24.
Email: info@folens.ie

Poland: JUKA, ul. Renesansowa 38, Warsaw 01-905.

Editor: Janice Baiton   Layout artist: Book Matrix, India   Illustrations: Tony Randell
Cover design: Holbrook Design   Cover image: Mary Evans Picture Library

First published 2006 by Folens Limited.

British Library Cataloguing in Publication Data. A catalogue record for this publication is available from the British Library.

ISBN 1-84303-967-2

Contents

Introduction

Specials! History have been specifically written for teachers to use with students who may struggle with some of the skills and concepts needed for Key Stage 3 History. The titles are part of a wider series from Folens for use with lower ability students.

Each book in the series contains ten separate units covering the topics needed to complete the theme of the book. Each unit has one or more photocopiable resource pages and several activity sheets. This allows the teacher to work in different ways. The tasks are differentiated throughout the book and offer all students the opportunity to expand their skills. Hopefully, by using photocopiable writing frames and emphasising literacy skills, students will be able to access historical information more easily.

The teacher's page at the start of each unit gives guidance on the material and is laid out as follows.

Objectives

These are the main skills or knowledge to be learned.

Prior knowledge

This refers to the minimum skills or knowledge required by students to complete the tasks. As a rule, students should have a reading comprehension age of 6 to 9 years and should be working at levels 1 to 3. Some activity sheets are more challenging than others and teachers will need to select accordingly.

QCA and NC links; Scottish attainment targets

All units link to the QCA Schemes of Work and to the NC for History at Key Stage 3. There are also links to the Scottish 5–14 guidelines.

Background

This provides additional information for the teacher, expanding on historical details or giving further information about the unit.

Starter activity

Since the units can be taught as a lesson, a warm-up activity focusing on an aspect of the unit is suggested.

Resource sheets and activity sheets

The resource sheets, which are often visual but may also be written, do not include tasks and can be used as stimulus for discussion. Related tasks are provided on the activity sheets.

Where necessary, keywords are included on the student pages. Other keywords are included on the teacher's page. These can be introduced to students at the teacher's discretion and depending on students' abilities.

Assessment sheet

At the end of each unit is an assessment sheet focusing on student progress. It can be used in different ways. A student can complete it as a self-assessment, while the teacher also completes one on each student's progress. They can then compare the two. This is useful in situations where the teacher or classroom assistant is working with one student. Alternatively, students can work in pairs to carry out peer assessments and then compare the outcomes with each other. Starting from a simple base that students can manage, the assessment sheet allows the student to discuss their own progress, to consider different points of view and to discuss how they might improve, thus enabling the teacher to see the work from the student's perspective.

Plenary

The teacher can use the suggestions here to recap on the main points covered or to reinforce a particular idea.

Look out for other titles in the History series, which include:
- The Romans
- Medieval Britain 1066–1485
- Changing Britain 1485–1750
- Britain in the 20th Century

Teacher's notes

Why did the British population grow?

Objectives

- Learn the different reasons why the British population rose
- Understand how population growth affected British society
- Be able to rank ideas in order of importance
- Learn how the connective 'because' can help to further explain what we think
- Understand and use the key term 'population growth'

Prior knowledge

Students need to be aware that, during the Industrial Revolution, Britain was divided into new industrial towns and rural agricultural societies.

QCA link

Unit 11 Industrial changes action and reaction

NC links

History skills 2c, 5b

Scottish attainment target

Environmental Studies – Society – People in the past Strand – Change and continuity, cause and effect Level D, Level E

Background

The British population was estimated at approximately 7 million people in 1750 and was rising very slowly. It had increased to 21 million people by 1851 and to 37 million people by 1901. By the late nineteenth century the British population was either living in urban towns, where the population increase was at its highest, or in rural villages, where population levels were growing more slowly. Two things were happening to encourage population growth. First, more babies were being born and surviving into adulthood; and second, improved health and medicine was allowing people to live longer.

Starter activity

Introduce the key term 'population growth' and brainstorm with the students what they think it means. Encourage them to explain their answers in as much detail as possible.

Resource sheet and activity sheets

Present students with the resource sheet 'Industrial Revolution' and go through the keywords with them. The aim is for them to learn how to spell and use the keywords for this unit successfully.

'Causes of population growth' provides students with illustrations of the six main causes of population growth in Britain. Students cut out the causes and rank them in order of importance with teacher guidance. This can lead to class discussion if students rank them differently.

'Connecting the causes of population growth' is a follow-on activity from 'Causes of population growth'. It introduces students to connectives, allowing them to explain their decisions more fully; for example, why a cause is most or least important.

'Causes and consequences of population growth' allows students to discover the consequences of the six main causes of population growth. Students should link each cause to its consequence and then make decisions about the most/least important consequence.

Assessment sheet

Ask students to complete this sheet to evaluate their overall understanding of population growth during the Industrial Revolution and of the key skills developed.

Plenary

Lead a game of keyword hangman on the board to encourage students to use the new words from this topic.

Industrial Revolution

Britain's Industrial Revolution took place between 1750 and 1900. One of the main causes of the Industrial Revolution was population growth. Two very important questions that we have to ask are:

- What caused the population to grow?
- How did this growth affect the country?

In this unit you will learn about the six main causes of population growth. The box below has the keywords or phrases that you will find useful for this topic.

Keyword	Definition
Industrial Revolution	Britain's industry changed from farming to factories
population growth	the number of people in the country gets bigger
cause	a reason why something happens
factory	a big building where lots of people make things
industry	the way a country makes its money
consequences	what happens after an event takes place
hygiene	keeping things clean to promote good health
sanitation	running water and flushing toilets
diet	what people eat
wages	the amount of money that people are paid

By learning about the Industrial Revolution you are learning about people's lives. This can be a fantastic and interesting topic to study.

Causes of population growth

A *cause* is a reason why something happens.

 You are going to learn about what caused the British population to grow between 1750 and 1900. Cut out the pictures below that show the different causes of population growth. Now work with a partner to place them in the order that you both think is most important. This means putting the one that you both think is the most important at the top and the one that you both think is the least important at the bottom.

People got married younger and could have children sooner.

Cleaner water was available.

New medicine stopped people dying young.

More people had jobs in factories.

People had more money.

People had better diets.

Connecting the causes of population growth

Connectives are words that link up sentences. They make your writing more detailed. The easiest connective is *because* and in this lesson you will use it to explain which cause of population growth you think is the most important and which is the least important.

☞ In pairs, study the 'Causes of population growth' cards that you both sorted into order of importance last lesson. Together you must now explain why you both think that one of the causes is very important and why one is the least important. On a separate sheet of paper, copy and complete the templates below to help you explain what you think. You should both complete a template each.

> **Handy hint:** You need to think about how the causes would have helped more people to live longer or have helped more babies to be born.

Most important cause of population growth

> I think that _____ was the most important cause of population growth in the eighteenth century **because** _____
> _____
> _____
> _____
> _____
> _____

Least important cause of population growth

> I think that _____ was the least important cause of population growth in the eighteenth century **because** _____
> _____
> _____
> _____
> _____
> _____

When you have written your answers, look back at the 'Causes of population growth' resource sheet and draw a picture on your sheet that matches your decision.

Causes and consequences of population growth

What impact did the causes of population growth have on Britain?

Britain's population growth came about because of six main causes. These causes are on the left side of the box below. On the right side of the box are the consequences of the causes. This means how they affected people. Look at the consequences carefully because they are all mixed up.

Causes	Consequences
1. People married younger.	a) People could now drink and cook food without fear of dirty water.
2. Cleaner water became available.	b) A better diet meant that people could eat more healthily and live longer.
3. New medicine was invented.	c) By marrying younger, people could have children at an earlier age.
4. New factories were built.	d) Factories paid people more money that helped them improve their lives.
5. People had more money.	e) If people became sick, then new medicine gave them more chance of getting better and living longer.
6. People had better diets.	f) They could spend their extra money on more food and warm clothing.

☞ Read through the CAUSES and CONSEQUENCES above very carefully.

1. Draw a line from each cause to its matching consequence.

2. Which CONSEQUENCE do you think is the MOST important? Use a coloured pen to shade this CONSEQUENCE.

3. In the box below, explain why you think this CONSEQUENCE helped the population to grow the most. There is no right or wrong answer.

Assessment sheet – Why did the British population grow?

✓ Tick the boxes to show what you know.

I know:

	Yes	Not sure	Don't know
what Industrial Revolution means			
what population growth means			
what caused the population to grow			
how population growth affected Britain			
what a connective is			
what the keywords mean			
how to spell the keywords			

One thing that I remember the most about this unit is:

_____

_____

_____

New keywords that I have learned:

Specials! History Industrial Britain 1750–1900   © Folens (copiable page)

Teacher's notes

How did British transport develop?

Objectives

● Understand how different forms of transport developed in Britain

● Understand the dangers of new forms of transport

● Learn essay writing skills and the use of keywords

Prior knowledge

Students need to be aware that a growing population in Great Britain meant that people now wanted to move around the country more and also this meant that a better system of communication and transport was needed.

QCA link

Unit 11 Industrial changes action and reaction

NC links

History skills 2c, 2e

Scottish attainment targets

Environmental Studies – Society – People in the past
Strand – People, events and societies of significance in the past
Level E

Background

Between 1750 and 1900, Britain's transport changed dramatically. With the development of factories and the growth of industry it became necessary for raw materials to reach factories quickly and cheaply. In addition, factory owners needed to transport their goods for export abroad. As new methods of travel became available, such as roads, canals and railways, the structure of Britain's communication and transport system became faster, more efficient and cheaper. This helped Britain to become the 'Workshop of the World'.

Starter activity

Give students a copy of the activity sheet 'Early eighteenth-century roads'. In pairs, they should spend two minutes working out the problems that existed with roads in eighteenth-century Britain. When the two minutes are up, ask the students to brainstorm as a class about the problems with early roads and write their results on the board.

Resource sheets and activity sheets

'Trust the rich to fix the roads' explains how new roads were improved by turnpikes. Read through the sheet and discuss the diagram with the class.

'Liverpool to Manchester Railway' explains why businessmen wanted to build a new railway and gives arguments for and against the railway.

'Highwaymen and pirates' is a simple and self-explanatory activity sheet about the actions of highwaymen and pirates.

'What is the Duke of Bridgewater famous for?' explains why the Duke of Bridgewater built the first canal and how it improved travel. The activity calls for designing a poster advertising the Bridgewater Canal – emphasise the written aspect of the poster as well as the drawing.

The 'Liverpool to Manchester Railway Speech' activity sheet illustrates how a speech should be set out. Students should fill in the gaps in the speech from the word bank.

Assessment sheet

Students complete this sheet to evaluate their overall understanding of transport development during the Industrial Revolution and of the key skills developed.

Plenary

Ask for volunteers to come to the front of the classroom and be 'put under the spotlight' on one of the topics that has just been studied. Students have to talk for approximately 20 seconds on a topic.

Early eighteenth-century roads

What were the problems with early eighteenth-century roads?

Many people did not like using British roads in the eighteenth century. They were poorly built, dangerous to travel on and did not link up all the main towns and cities in the country.

☞ In pairs, examine the two pictures below. Use a coloured pen to circle all the problems that you think early roads had. Then on the back of this activity sheet, write two sentences explaining what you think the problems were with early roads.

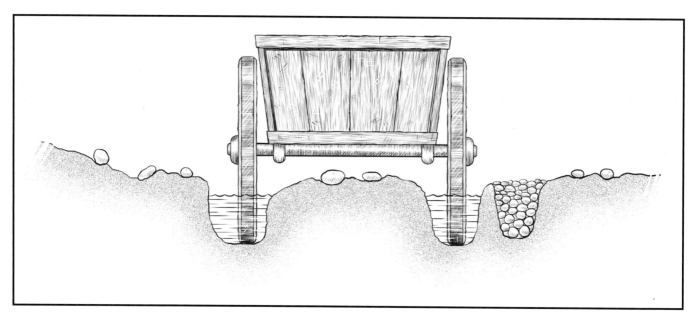

Trust the rich to fix the roads

Great Britain's roads needed to be improved. The first important change began in 1663 when the first Turnpike Trust was set up by a group of rich businessmen.

A Turnpike Trust was a simple idea – people who used the roads should pay for the roads. Businessmen paid professional road builders to design the best route for the road and then built it.

They built toll gates at each end of the road and charged people money to use it. Any money that they made was used to keep the road in good condition. Look at the picture below to see all the advantages of new turnpiked roads.

1 Toll gates where money was collected
2 New bridges built over streams
3 Roads had a better surface
4 Roads were straighter and more level
5 Professional road builders were employed

These new roads made transporting goods and people around the country faster and cheaper. People were very happy with the new system of transport.

But some people did not always like the new roads. Many businessmen did not use the money from the tolls to keep the roads in good condition but spent it on themselves instead. People also did not like spending money to use roads that they had always used for free.

Highwaymen and pirates

Danger on the roads

The new roads had problems. With more stagecoaches travelling on British roads, you might meet highwaymen.

Highwaymen went around the country robbing stagecoaches. They wore masks and ordered people to give them all their money. They did not usually kill the passengers.

The most famous highwayman was a man called Dick Turpin. Read the text below to see just how bad Dick Turpin really was.

Dick Turpin jumped out from behind a hedge, pointed his pistol at the stagecoach driver and shouted 'Your money or your life!' He pulled open the coach door, dragged out the nearest woman, yanked a necklace from around her neck and then threw her to the ground. The woman was crying with fear.

Safer on the seas?

Some people travelled by sea and used a boat to sail around the British coast. It was faster, smoother and cheaper but they had to watch out for pirates. Many British ships found themselves boarded by pirates who were not as nice as Captain Jack Sparrow in *The Pirates of the Caribbean*. They stole money and food and often left people to die on the boats after they had gone.

 Answer the questions below.

1. What did a highwayman do?
2. Why do you think that highwaymen wore masks?
3. Who would you rather be attacked by – highwaymen or pirates? Give two reasons why you chose either a highwayman or a pirate.

What is the Duke of Bridgewater famous for?

The Duke of Bridgewater was very important to British transport in the eighteenth century. He is remembered for one important thing:

He was the first man to pay for a canal to be built in Britain.

Why did he need to build a canal?

In the eighteenth century, it cost a lot of money to transport coal by road. This was because it was heavy. The Duke of Bridgewater owned a coalmine in Worsley but he could not find a cheap way to transport his coal to Manchester. This made his coal expensive and people would not buy it. He had to find a cheap way to move it.

He asked a man called James Brindley to build him a man-made river called a canal. This canal linked Bridgewater's mines at Worsley to Manchester. He then sailed a canal boat along it filled with coal. This saved him money and more people bought his coal.

His canal was cheaper than using turnpikes. His canal was smoother than roads so less things broke. His canal was faster than using roads. He made a lot of money from it.

☞ Imagine that you have been asked by the Duke of Bridgewater to design a poster advertising his new canal. You must convince people to use the Bridgewater Canal by explaining why it would be better than using roads.

On a separate sheet of paper, design a poster showing the new canal and include information about it being cheaper, faster and easier to use canals.

Liverpool to Manchester Railway

During the early nineteenth century, two of the most important towns in Britain were Manchester and Liverpool.

Raw materials arrived by boat at Liverpool docks and were transported by road or canal to factories in Manchester. This was too slow and businessmen in the two towns needed a newer and faster type of transport.

In 1822, they decided to build a railway line between Liverpool and Manchester. Some people were happy but others were not.

Arguments against the Liverpool to Manchester Railway

- 10 mph would be too fast for humans.
- Trains might make cows fall over.
- Pregnant women might lose their babies.
- Sparks from trains might set farms on fire.
- People might choke to death on the train's smoke.
- Canal and road businesses would be ruined.

People who hated the railway were canal owners, road builders, the Duke of Bridgewater and farmers along the route.

Arguments for the Liverpool to Manchester Railway

- It would be cheaper.
- It would be faster.
- It would be a more direct route.
- Factories would make more money.
- Ship owners would make more money.

People who supported railways included ship owners and factory owners in Leeds and Manchester.

Liverpool to Manchester Railway speech

☞ Complete the speech below supporting the new Liverpool to Manchester Railway by using the words from the wordbank to fill in the blanks.

Wordbank

Liverpool	Railway	Manchester	products	money	raw
break	pirates	tolls	highwaymen	Trusts	

Dear Sir/Madam

I am here today to tell you about the new and fantastic _____ to _____ Railway that has been built by George Stephenson.

It was opened in 1830 and could save you lots of _____. You can send your goods to Manchester much faster and less items will _____. You do not have to stop along the route to pay _____ at Turnpike _____. You do not have to worry about _____ or _____ robbing you.

Factories can buy _____ materials more cheaply and sell _____ for more money. This is a fantastic way to travel.

So please use the Liverpool to Manchester _____.

A. Burke

Assessment sheet – How did British transport develop?

✓ Tick the boxes to show what you know.

I know:	Yes	Not sure	Don't know
what a Turnpike Trust is			
what made travelling by road or sea dangerous			
what the Duke of Bridgewater did			
why people were for and against the London to Manchester Railway			
what a speech is			
how to design an informative poster			
how to correctly identify the keywords			

The thing that I remember the most about this unit is:

_____

_____

_____

The best type of transport was _____

because_____

_____

Teacher's notes

Growth of factories

Objectives

- Learn the different reasons why factories in Britain increased
- Understand why people in Britain worked mainly in factories during the eighteenth century
- Understand the importance of British factories to the growth of the Empire

Prior knowledge

Students need to be aware that transport development during the Industrial Revolution encouraged the movement of raw materials and finished products around Britain, which meant that the number of factories in Britain grew.

QCA link

Unit 11 Industrial changes action and reaction

NC links

History skills 4b, 7d, 10

Scottish attainment targets

Environmental Studies – Society – People in the past Strand – Change and continuity, cause and effect Level E

Background

During the eighteenth century, Britain changed from a rural agricultural economy to an urban factory system. The increase in cheap, raw materials entering Britain through ports such as Liverpool made it possible for businessmen – such as Josiah Wedgwood and Samuel Greg – to make products cheaply that could then be sold for huge profits. These businessmen built factories to make their new products and this allowed many people in Britain to find work away from farms.

Starter activity

Write the word 'Factory' on the board and ask the students to brainstorm about what they think this word means and what type of work they think people undertake in factories.

Resource sheets and activity sheets

'The growth of textile factories' is a basic read-through fact sheet about the change from the domestic system to working in factories using power looms. Use the sheet to make sure students understand the keywords and encourage them to fill in the definitions themselves.

'Workshop of the world' explains how the Empire helped factories to expand and make Britain become the 'Workshop of the World'.

'The importance of raw materials' introduces students to the concept of raw materials. Read the top paragraph with the class and use items in the room to illustrate the idea of raw materials, then ask the students to complete the chart at the bottom of the sheet.

'The growth of textile factories diagram' is a follow-on activity from 'The growth of textile factories' resource sheet. Use the resource sheet to encourage the students to complete the simple tasks on the diagram.

'Great Exhibition poster' is a follow-on activity from the 'Workshop of the world' resource sheet. Ask the students to use the resource sheet to complete this activity. Emphasise the key features of a poster – price, place and what you can see.

Assessment sheet

Ask students to complete the assessment sheet to see how much they can remember.

Plenary

Students can play a game of 'History Bingo'. Ask them to draw a nine-square bingo grid on a piece of paper and fill it with keywords you have chosen from this unit. Read out the meanings of the words and the students cross out the words when they think you have described them. Standard bingo rules follow at this point.

The importance of raw materials

Raw materials are used to make things that you buy. The table that you are working on is made of wood, which is a raw material. You can make lots of things if the raw material is cheap. When you sell the product, you can make a big profit and that makes people rich. In the eighteenth century, cheap raw material arrived in Britain from other countries. People built factories and employed workers to make lots of useful things from these raw materials.

☞ Look at the pictures below. They show raw materials that came to Britain. Work out what they are and what they could be used for. When you have done this, fill in the boxes below the pictures. The first one has been done for you.

A   B   C   D   E

Picture	What you think it is	What it was used for
Picture A	Clay	To make pottery
Picture B		
Picture C		
Picture D		
Picture E		

Specials! History Industrial Britain 1750–1900
© Folens (copiable page)

The growth of textile factories

Keywords

factories _____

domestic system _____

power loom _____

Why did factories grow?

Many people in Britain worked from home before 1750. This was called the **domestic system**. Cheap raw material such as wool came from America and was made into cloth. This was done by hand. This cloth was then made into clothes and people paid a lot of money for them. After 1750, rich businessmen built **factories**, which were big buildings where lots of people could make goods in one place. They used new machines to do this and did not do it by hand. People no longer worked at home because factories made goods like cloth much more cheaply.

What happened in a factory?

A man called Edmund Cartwright invented a new machine called a **power loom** in 1785. It used a water wheel to power it because electricity had not been invented yet. The new power loom was used to make cotton cloth very quickly and cheaply.

Who worked in these factories?

You may think that being at school everyday is boring. During the Industrial Revolution, students aged 11 to 14 had to work in factories with their parents. This was because the new power looms were easy to use. Employers could pay women and children less than men.

The power looms also broke down sometimes. Adults were too big to fit under the machines. Children were small enough to fit under the large power looms and had small fingers that could reach inside the power loom to repair it. You just had to hope that the machine did not start up again before you got your hand out!

Activity sheet – Growth of factories

The growth of textile factories diagram

☞ Look at 'The growth of textile factories' resource sheet to help you complete this diagram.

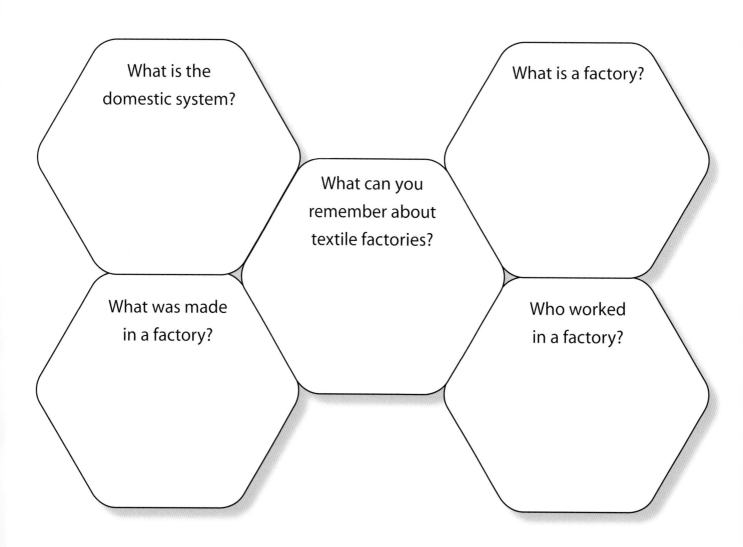

What is the domestic system?

What can you remember about textile factories?

What is a factory?

What was made in a factory?

Who worked in a factory?

☞ Why was it dangerous for children to work with power looms? Write an answer on the lines below.

_____

_____

_____

_____

Resource sheet – Growth of factories

Workshop of the world

Britain had a big empire in the eighteenth century. This meant that it was in charge of lots of countries around the world such as India and Canada.

People in these countries sold cheap raw material, such as cotton and wood, to Britain. British factories then made them into other items such as clothes and furniture. They sold these new items for more money.

By 1851, there were so many British factories making products that were sold all over the Empire that Britain was given the name 'Workshop of the World'. Queen Victoria's husband, Prince Albert, set up a show called the Great Exhibition in 1851 to show people how amazing Britain was.

A large glass building was built in Hyde Park in London. They called it Crystal Palace. It was 500 metres long and 125 metres wide and was open for five months. It had:

- 13 000 exhibits
- a circus
- the biggest piano in the world
- dinosaur skeletons
- trees that went through the roof.

Over six million people visited the Great Exhibition. It only cost one shilling (5p) to get in, so everybody was able to visit it.

Great Exhibition poster

☞ Imagine you have been asked by Prince Albert to design a poster for the Great Exhibition. You must give people all the information that they would need before planning a visit. Think about:

- where it is
- what people can see
- how much it costs to go in.

Remember pictures always make you look at something more closely.

Assessment sheet – Growth of factories

Use this sheet to see how much you can remember about the growth of factories in Britain during the Industrial Revolution.

| ✓ | Tick the sentences below that are true. |

| X | Put a cross next to the sentences that are false. |

| British factories never used raw materials. | |

| The domestic system meant working in a factory. | |

| Woman and children were employed in factories because they were paid less. | |

| An empire was a big factory. | |

| Britain was called the 'Workshop of the World'. | |

| The Great Exhibition was held in 1851. | |

| It was Queen Victoria's idea to build Crystal Palace. | |

| It cost £5 to enter the 'Great Exhibition'. | |

Factory working conditions

Objectives

- Establish empathy with contemporary historical figures
- Understand exactly how bad working conditions were for children in factories
- Develop literary skills through using writing frames

Prior knowledge

Students need to be aware that children were employed in nineteenth-century factories from a very early age and were paid very little money.

QCA link

Unit 11 Industrial changes action and reaction

NC links

History skills 4a, 6c

Scottish attainment targets

Environmental Studies – Society – People in the past
Strand – People, events and societies of significance in the past
Level E

Starter activity

Say a letter out loud and members of the class should respond with a keyword from the 'Growth of factories' unit beginning with that letter.

Resource sheets and activity sheets

The resource sheets 'Joseph Kelly's story 1 and 2' are a simple story of a pauper apprentice called Joseph Kelly. Read through the story with the class emphasising the keywords in bold.

'An inspector calls' is a straightforward interview activity, where the students complete an interview writing frame using information taken from the story.

'The final report' is a slightly harder activity that encourages students to use the information they have looked at so far to complete some cloze sentences and suggest improvements to factory working conditions.

Assessment sheet

Students should complete this simple assessment sheet to establish what skills have been developed and to what competency.

Plenary

Say a letter out loud and members of the class should respond with a keyword from this unit beginning with that letter.

Background

With the textile industry in Britain changing from the domestic system to the factory system, a new and cheap labour force was needed. During the eighteenth and nineteenth centuries, factory owners employed children and pauper apprentices to work in their factories. Many of these children were badly treated and poorly paid. The work in factories and textile mills was very dangerous and many children lost limbs before factory reformers changed British laws to help children.

Joseph Kelly's story (1)

Over the next two pages is a story about a young child called Joseph Kelly. He worked in a textile factory during the nineteenth century. Read the following story and you will learn about what it was like to work in a textile factory.

The story

Joseph was only eight when his mum and dad died. He had nobody to look after him. Joseph was sent to an **orphanage**.

Joseph made friends with a boy called Andrew. One day they were told that they were leaving the orphanage to go and work in a **factory**.

John Boughey was the owner of the factory and he employed children because they were cheap. Children were easy to teach and easy to control. He needed them to work at his factory for a long time if he was to make a **profit**.

Joseph and Andrew became **pauper apprentices**. This meant that they would work all day in the factory and sleep at night in an apprentice house. They were not very happy working at the factory.

Joseph and Andrew were made to get up every morning at 5:30am. They were given a lump of porridge in their hand to eat as they walked to the factory. They would not eat again until 1:00pm.

Their job was to crawl under the **power looms** to fix the cotton threads if they broke. Their hands were small enough to fit into the machines. They had to be quick or the machines would cut off their fingers. This work was very dangerous.

Working in the factory was very unhealthy. There were no windows and the machines made a lot of dust. The boys swallowed this dust and often felt sick.

Pauper apprentices were not allowed to take a day off work if they were sick or sit down at work. If they sat down, an **overseer** called Mr Duckworth punished them.

The pauper apprentices were frightened of Mr Duckworth. He enjoyed punishing them if they did not work hard enough.

He used a stick to beat them if they were slow. If he thought they were lazy, he would pick them up by their feet and dunk them head first into a barrel of water.

Specials! History Industrial Britain 1750–1900

Joseph Kelly's story (2)

One day Joseph was working by himself when he heard a loud and terrible noise in the factory. It sounded like a trapped animal screaming.

He crawled out from under the loom that he was fixing and looked around the room. He saw a big group of people standing by one of the large machines that broke down a lot. Suddenly the screaming stopped.

The screaming had been coming from the middle of the crowd. Joseph ran over to the crowd and pushed his way to the front. Some of the crowd held their hands over their faces. One of the girls, Rebecca, grabbed Joseph's hand and tried to stop him looking at the machine.

Mr Duckworth was trying to turn the machine off. The big machine was still working but something was trapped in it. Every time the machine started to work a red rag was slowing it down. Joseph started to scream.

When he had left the apprentice house that morning with Andrew they had both been wearing blue shirts. At the end of the red rag that was stopping the machine was a scrap of blue. Joseph could not see Andrew anywhere.

One of the older girls called Jacqueline hugged Joseph and told him what had happened.

Andrew was fixing a broken thread underneath the power loom when it suddenly started to work again.

Andrew pulled his hand out but the needles on the machined snagged his shirt and slowly pulled Andrew into the dangerous machine.

Joseph had heard Andrew screaming as he died.

People were very upset in the factory. But after an hour, Mr Boughey told everybody to get back to work or any money that was lost would be taken from their **wages**.

Joseph was very upset about his best friend. Andrew was not the first person to die at the factory and he would not be the last. Factories were a very dangerous place to work. Somebody needed to make them safer.

An inspector calls

By the 1830s, working conditions in some British factories were so bad that an investigation was started by Parliament. Inspectors were sent around the country in 1832 to report on working conditions in factories.

☞ You are going to pretend to be a factory inspector. You have a list of questions for Joseph Kelly about working conditions in his factory. Complete the report below to give to your bosses. Use Joseph's story to help you.

1832 Factory Report
Interviewer: Mr G. Rogers
Interviewee: Joseph Kelly

1. What time did you get up to start work at the factory?

   _____

2. What were you given to eat before you went to work at the factory?

   _____

3. Why were so many children given jobs at the factory?

   _____

4. What was your job at the factory?

   _____

5. Were children treated nicely at your factory? Give an example.

   _____

   _____

6. Has anybody ever been hurt at your factory? Give an example.

   _____

   _____

The final report

☞ You have read Joseph Kelly's story and completed an interview with Joseph Kelly. Now you must explain to Parliament what you would change about factory working conditions. Use the writing frame below to help you.

My conclusions about the condition of some British factories

From the evidence that I collected from Joseph Kelly at the Boughey Textile Factory, I believe that the following four changes need to be made to factories in Great Britain.

1. _____

2. _____

3. _____

4. _____

The reasons why I would make these changes are:

1. Children are too _____ to work in a factory.

2. Children have to get up too _____ to go to work.

3. Children are not given enough _____ to eat.

4. The work that children do is too _____.

5. Children often feel _____ from the dust in the factory.

6. Overseers are _____ to the children.

7. Children can _____ if they get caught in the machinery.

Assessment sheet – Factory working conditions

✓ Tick the boxes to show what you know.

I know:

	Yes	Not sure	Don't know
what a pauper apprentice is			
what an overseer is			
why children were employed in factories			
how dangerous it was to work in factories			
how an interview works			
how to use a writing frame properly			
how to identify key words			

One thing that I remember the most about this unit is:

_____

_____

_____

New keywords that I have learned:

Teacher's notes

Factory reformers

Objectives

- Understand who the different factory reformers were
- Appreciate different points of contemporary views
- Use sources effectively

Prior knowledge

Students need to be aware that during the Industrial Revolution working conditions in textile factories were so poor that people campaigned to get them improved.

QCA link

Unit 11 Industrial changes action and reaction

NC links

History skills 4a, 7a

Scottish attainment targets

Environmental Studies – Society – People in the past Strand – Change and continuity, cause and effect Level E

Background

Factories had been employing children and pauper apprentices for many years. However, by 1832 many people in Britain believed that working conditions for both women and children in factories was dangerous and unhealthy. Some people argued that many factories treated their pauper apprentices very well. Some gave them excellent food, allowed them to work short hours and even provided them with an education. During the nineteenth century, reformers campaigned to get factories improved. This unit will look at this aspect of the Industrial Revolution.

Starter activity

Brainstorm with students about working conditions for children in factories based on work from the previous unit.

Resource sheets and activity sheets

'Factory reformers' provides source material for the activity sheet 'Factory reformers' work'.

Read through the information on 'Samuel Greg and Styal Mill' and then help the students to complete the tasks on activity sheet 'Samuel Greg's letter to Parliament'.

'Why people disagreed about factories' provides several reasons for and against reform. Students fill in the table using the information provided.

'Factory reformers' work' contains a true-or-false activity for students to complete using the information from the sources in the resource sheet 'Factory reformers'.

Complete the letter in 'Samuel Greg's letter to Parliament' using the information in resource sheet 'Samuel Greg and Styal Mill'.

Provide the students with scissors for the paired activity in 'Factory reforms'.

Assessment sheet

Ask students to complete the assessment sheets to see how much they can remember about this unit.

Plenary

Lead a game of keyword hangman on the board to encourage students to use the new words from this unit.

Why people disagreed about factories

By the 1830s some people in Britain did not like the way that workers were being treated in factories. Some people said that factory workers had to **work long hours** in **dangerous conditions**. They were very worried about how children were being treated. Some people said that pauper apprentices were **badly fed**. People were worried that children would grow up badly educated and deformed with **bad backs, missing arms and legs**. These people were called factory reformers.

There was another group of people who said that children were treated much better in factories than they were in orphanages or when working at home. They argued that many **pauper apprentices were better fed, learnt a skill** and some even **learnt how to read and write**. Many factory owners also built special houses for pauper apprentices to live in and had doctors look after their workforce.

☞ Use the information above to fill in the chart below. One reason is completed for you as an example of what to do.

Reasons for reform	Reasons against reform
Had to work long hours	Paupers were better fed

Factory reformers

Very famous factory reformers, such as a woman called Frances Trollope, wrote stories about the conditions for children in factories. They were very detailed and made people think that children were being treated very badly. Some of these stories were exaggerated and were not always truthful. Have a look at the source below, based on Frances Trollope's book about a factory boy called Michael Armstrong.

'As they entered the room, the dirty, ragged and miserable children were all working. The overseers stood with straps in their hands and made the little slaves work harder. These children were thin and they had sunken cheeks and hollow eyes. They looked very old.'

SOURCE A   Based on a Frances Trollope book

Factory reformers also included pictures of factory children with their writing. This was to make people who could not read feel guilty about the way that children were being treated. Look at the picture below.

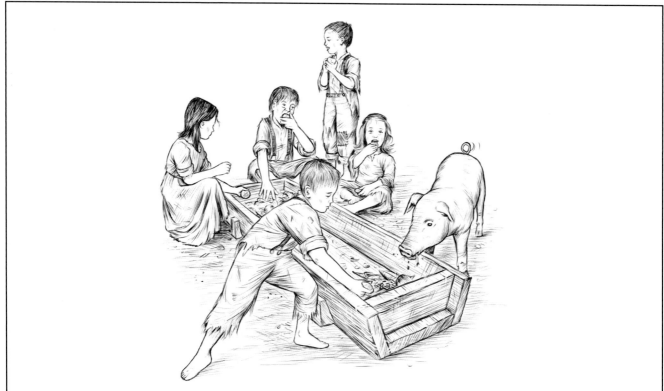

SOURCE B Based on illustration VI from *Michael Armstrong: Factory Boy*

Specials! History Industrial Britain 1750–1900   © Folens (copiable page)

Factory reformers' work

☞ Look carefully at the two sources on the resource sheet 'Factory reformers'. They are sources giving reasons why people felt that factories needed to be made better. What information can we find in the sources to support the factory reformer's point of view?

| ✓ | Tick the sentences below that are true. |

| X | Put a cross next to the sentences that are false. |

Frances Trollope believed that factory children were very clean and happy.	
Overseers were good adults who looked after the young children in the factories	
Pauper apprentices were thin and had sunken cheeks and hollow eyes.	
Pauper apprentices seemed to get very old very quickly.	
Everybody in Britain could read.	
The children in Source B look like they are eating from a pig's trough.	
The children in Source B are well dressed and well fed.	
Both Sources A and B are telling the truth.	

Samuel Greg and Styal Mill

Some people felt that children who worked in factories had better lives. A factory owner called Samuel Greg said that factories gave children a good life.

He let factory inspectors into his mill at Styal and they found that children and workers there were treated very well.

This is what the factory inspectors found.

- Wages at Styal Mill were good and people did not work long hours.
- Samuel Greg was a kind employer.
- Mr Greg built nice houses for his workers.
- It was very dangerous to work in factories.
- The paupers' apprentice house was large and clean.
- Pauper apprentices were given a little education.

Samuel Greg did not want factory reforms. He said that shorter hours would make products cost more. This would make Britain poorer. He also said that people who worked from home became very ill.

Samuel Greg was a factory owner and many people said that he did not want to lose money if Parliament changed working conditions. Not everything was fantastic at Styal Mill because some pauper apprentices ran away. A little girl called Esther Price ran away in 1835 and 1836.

In 1835 I ran away from Styal Mill. I missed my family and went to Liverpool to see them. I did not ask Mr Greg if I could go to see my mum and dad.

I was forced to go back to Styal Mill. I still missed my parents so I ran away again in 1836.

When I was taken back to Styal Mill this time I was locked in a small room and they told me that if I ran away again they would cut my hair off.
This made me want to leave Styal Mill again.

Specials! History Industrial Britain 1750–1900

Samuel Greg's letter to Parliament

☞ Imagine that you are Samuel Greg and you are writing a letter to Parliament explaining why you think that factory working conditions should not change. In your letter you should mention the following things:

- who you are
- what you do
- why all factories are not bad – give examples of good things about your factory.

Dear Parliament

I do not think that you should change working conditions in factories because

_____

_____

_____

_____

_____

_____

_____

_____

From Samuel Greg

Factory reforms

☞ Work in pairs for this activity. Cut out the cards. They show how working conditions in factories changed. Rank the cards in order from the most important change first down to the least important change. Write a timeline of them when you have finished.

Children were
to be taught to
read and write.
1802

Factory rooms
were to be
washed twice a
year.
1802

Children were not
allowed to work
more than 12
hours a day.
1802

Children could
not work at
night.
1833

Children aged 9 to
13 were not to work
more than nine hours
a day. Children aged
13 to 18 could work
no more than 12
hours a day.
1833

Accidents causing
death or maiming
were reported
to doctors who
investigated their cause
and reported the result
to the inspector.
1844

Children should
go to school two
hours a day.
1833

No child workers
under nine years old.
Employers had an
age certificate for
child workers.
1833

Dangerous
machinery
now had to be
fenced in.
1844

Assessment sheet – Factory reformers

✓ Tick the boxes to show what you know.

I know:	Yes	Not sure	Don't know
why factory reformers wanted improvements			
what a source is			
why people wanted to keep children in factories			
what improvements were made to factories			
reasons for and against an argument			
how to use a letter writing frame properly			
how to rank ideas in order of importance			

One thing that I remember the most about this unit is:

_____

_____

_____

_____

Teacher's notes

Lousy living conditions

Objectives

- Learn the different reasons why living conditions were so poor
- Understand the importance of clean water for people's health

Prior knowledge

Students need to be aware that the number of people in Britain grew during the Industrial Revolution. As a result of this, living conditions worsened.

QCA link

Unit 11 Industrial changes action and reaction

NC links

History skills 2a, 2b, 3a, 4b

Scottish attainment targets

Environmental Studies – Society – People in the past
Strand – The nature of historical evidence
Level E
Strand – Change and continuity, cause and effect
Level D

Starter activity

Students should play hangman on the board using words or key phrases from previous units. An emphasis should be placed on the correct spelling of keywords.

Resource sheet and activity sheets

Read through the resource sheet 'Poor housing' with the students.

Students use the 'Poor housing' resource sheet to answer the simple source questions on activity sheet 'Why were living conditions so bad?'.

'Stinky sewers' is a question and answer sheet about the condition of sewers during the Industrial Revolution.

Assessment sheet

A combined assessment sheet for this unit and the next appears at the end of the 'Woeful water' unit. Students complete this when both units have been covered.

Plenary

Students should play pictionary – ask for some volunteers to 'draw' a keyword on the whiteboard and the rest of the class should guess what it is.

Background

The growth of population and towns during the eighteenth century meant that many houses were built quickly and poorly. Sanitation and living conditions were very poor and people's health was atrocious.

Poor housing

Lots of people lived in towns during the Industrial Revolution. They lived in towns because they worked in factories. So many people lived in towns that there were not enough houses. Builders wanted to make a lot of money so they built cheap houses quickly.

These houses were built very badly and it cost a lot of money to rent a room. A whole family would live in one room. Everybody could see what you were doing. Houses had no toilets or running water. Disease spread very quickly.

The sources below show just how bad industrial towns were.

Houses were built back to back. Families rented just one room in a house. Sometimes two families shared a room. The walls were damp and the ceiling was black. The floor was rotten. Every stairway was full with children. Their clothes had holes. They had no shoes. They were filthy and full of lice.

Source A A school textbook

Look at that great hole in the floor. The landlord will not fix it. People have to watch every night because rats come out of the sewer. If they do not watch for rats, they would eat the baby.

Source B A rich man visiting Liverpool in 1847

Sewage and rubbish was piled up at the end of the street. It fell into the local river where people drank water from.

Source C A school textbook

I visited a poor woman who had just had a baby. She and the baby were lying on straw in a cellar. There was no light and the air was bad. I walked across bricks on the floor to reach her bed as the floor was flooded with water.

Source D Description of conditions in Liverpool in 1843 by R Birkett-Evans

Why were living conditions bad?

☞ Use the information from Sources A to D on the resource sheet 'Poor housing' to answer the following questions. Write your answers in the space provided.

1. What were rooms like during the Industrial Revolution?

    During the Industrial Revolution rooms were_____

    _____

    _____

2. Using Source A, list three ways that show how poor children were in Liverpool.

    a) _____

    b) _____

    c) _____

3. What animal often came out of sewers during the night?

    _____

4. Look at Source D. Find four things that would be bad for a newborn baby.

    a) _____

    b) _____

    c) _____

    d) _____

Stinky sewers

Most houses did not have running water. People used a tap at the end of the street.

Most houses did not have a toilet. There would be a toilet for everybody to use at the end of the street. It did not empty into a drain but was left to run freely down the street.

Sometimes the toilet and the tap for drinking water were next to each other.

This was very unhealthy.

☞ Read the description of a nineteenth-century toilet below and then answer the questions in the space provided.

> At the end of the street was the privy. This was an old toilet that everybody had to use. It was not emptied for days and was very smelly. The toilet was just a wooden seat with a hole it in. You could see flies buzzing all around it. The waste slid under the toilet and into the drinking water nearby.
>
> **Source A** A Liverpool toilet

1. What would a person today think of a toilet like the one in Source A?

_____

_____

2. What do YOU think was the worst thing about toilets in the nineteenth century?

_____

_____

Teacher's notes

Woeful water

Objectives

- Learn the condition of water in Britain during the Industrial Revolution
- Understand why water was in such bad condition
- Understand how health and hygiene affect people's lives

Prior knowledge

Students need to be aware that as factory towns grew, clean water was desperately needed.

QCA link

Unit 11 Industrial changes action and reaction

NC links

History skills 2a, 4a

Scottish attainment targets

Environmental Studies – Society – People in the past
Strand – Change and continuity, cause and effect
Level E

Starter activity

Encourage students to discuss what they use water for and how important it is for everyday life and health.

Resource sheet and activity sheets

Read through the information about the quality of water in 'Why the water was bad' with the students. Emphasise the keywords and encourage students to fill in the definitions themselves.

'All about water' contains an activity where students need to match the end of a sentence with its beginning.

Assessment sheet

Students should complete this sheet to evaluate their overall understanding of living conditions and sanitation during the Industrial Revolution and of the key skills developed.

Plenary

Students should play pictionary – for some volunteers to 'draw' a keyword on the whiteboard and the rest of the class should guess what it is.

Background

Overcrowding, disease and poor ventilation made it very unhealthy to live in factory towns during the nineteenth century. One of the worst aspects of living in a town was having a poor water supply. There was no running water in the towns and many people were forced to drink from polluted rivers and streams. In the worst cases, people had to buy clean water in buckets on the street.

Why the water was bad

Keywords

unhygienic	_____
disease	_____
germs	_____
sewer	_____

The water supply in Britain during the Industrial Revolution was very bad. Most people got their drinking water from rivers or streams. They used this water for drinking, washing and cooking food.

Using river water for washing and cooking was bad because most people dumped their rubbish in the river. Many people also emptied their toilets into the river as well. This made river water very **unhygienic**.

Later, when **sewers** were built, they emptied into the local river as well.

Water carried **disease** and **germs**. Many people became sick during the nineteenth century from drinking and using unclean water.

If people lived in London and Manchester, they could buy buckets of 'clean' water from pipes in the street. This cost them about one shilling (5p) a week.

All about water

☞ Use the information on the resource sheet 'Why the water was bad' to match each sentence starter below with its correct ending.

Use a pencil to draw a line from each Head to its matching Tail.

Heads

1. The water supply in Great Britain

2. Most people got their drinking water

3. Most people dumped their rubbish

4. This made river water

5. Water carried disease

6. People became sick during the

7. People who lived in London

8. This cost them about

Tails

a) from rivers or streams.

b) in the river.

c) 5p a bucket.

d) and germs.

e) nineteenth century.

f) could buy buckets of 'clean' water.

g) very unhygienic.

h) was very bad.

Assessment sheet – Woeful water

✓ Tick the boxes to show what you know.

I know:

	Yes	Not sure	Don't know
what houses were like in the nineteenth century			
how bad water was during the 1800s			
why people became ill after drinking water			
what diseases and germs are			
how to read sources			
how to answer simple questions using sources			
how to link sentences together			

One thing that I remember the most about this unit is:

_____

_____

_____

_____

Teacher's notes

Medical conditions

Objectives

- Discover the state of medicine in Britain prior to the Industrial Revolution
- Learn about the development of medicine in Britain between 1750 and 1900
- Look at specific medical improvers such as Edward Jenner and the smallpox vaccine

Prior knowledge

Students need to be aware that during the Industrial Revolution new industrial towns created new medical problems that had to be solved if Britain was to maintain a healthy workforce.

QCA link

Unit 11 Industrial changes action and reaction

NC links

History skills 1a, 6c

Scottish attainment targets

Environmental Studies – Society – People in the past
Strand – Change and continuity, cause and effect
Level E

Starter activity

Write three or four keywords on the board. Students should create their own titles for the piece of work they are about to do, using all the keywords.

Resource sheet and activity sheets

'Medicine before 1750' provides simple details about medicine before 1750. Read through the sheet with the class.

'Sickly smallpox – symptoms' supplies some information about smallpox and Edward Jenner. Read through the sheet with the class.

'Sickly smallpox – saviour' and 'Sickly smallpox – letter' are linked activities explaining the concept of smallpox, the role of Edward Jenner and how people saw his new vaccination. More guided support for the students will be needed here.

Assessment sheet

Students should complete this sheet to evaluate their overall understanding of the medical developments during the Industrial Revolution and of the key skills developed.

Plenary

Lead a game of keyword hangman on the board to encourage students to use the new words from this topic.

Background

Just like the rapid improvements in transport and factory production, there was also a rapid development in medicine and health during the Industrial Revolution. Between 1750 and 1900 new drugs, vaccinations and sterilisation helped to improve and prolong the quality of health in Britain. Many of these new changes were met with fear.

Medicine before 1750

Health in England was very poor during the Industrial Revolution. Many babies died young and lots of people did not live long. This was because there was very little medicine around and doctors did not always know what they were doing.

Doctors

There were no real hospitals during the Industrial Revolution. People only went to doctors when they were really injured or dying. There were three types of doctors before 1750.

1. *Physicians* – doctors who treated disease.
2. *Surgeons* – doctors who operated on the outside of your body, such as cutting off an injured leg.
3. *Apothecaries* – doctors who made drugs.

These doctors did not always go to medical school. They also did not know what the inside of a human body looked like.

Medicine

Doctors did not know what caused diseases. They did not know about germs. If you were ill, they told you that there was something bad in your body. They would try and get rid of the bad thing.

Doctors believed that giving you drugs that would empty your stomach would make you better. There were two ways to empty your stomach.

1. Making you vomit.
2. Letting blood – cutting you so that all of the bad stuff came out in your blood.

Lots of people died from blood loss.

Class discussion points

- How happy would you be if your mum or dad took you to an eighteenth-century doctor?
- Would the doctor make you feel better?

Sickly smallpox – symptoms

One of the most dangerous diseases during the Industrial Revolution was smallpox. It killed almost 200 000 people between 1750 and 1900. When people caught smallpox they did not survive it.

Symptoms – how you could tell you were sick!

When people had smallpox they had fevers and headaches. After four days, their face, feet and hands became covered in a rash.

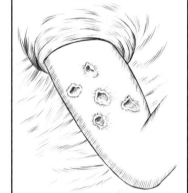

After a week the rash turned into blisters. Have a look at the picture on the right to see what the blisters looked like. When people got blisters they often died.

People who lived had bad marks on their faces where the blisters had been.

Edward Jenner

Edward Jenner was a doctor. He saw many people die from smallpox. Edward Jenner noticed another disease called cowpox. This was a disease caught by young girls who milked cows. These girls never caught smallpox. They were protected from it.

Edward Jenner took some pus from the blisters of cowpox victims and used a needle to inject it into an eight-year-old boy called James Phipps. He then injected James Phipps with smallpox but the boy did not catch it. Edward Jenner had discovered a vaccination for smallpox.

Many people did not like Edward Jenner's new discovery. Some people said that it would not work. Other people said that it would make people act like cows.

But it did work!

Class disscusion point

How would you feel if your doctor wanted to inject you with pus from an animal?

Sickly smallpox – saviour

☞ Below is a picture based on a famous painting by James Gillray showing Edward Jenner giving a smallpox vaccination. Take a good look at it.

1. Describe what you think is happening in the picture in the box below.

2. What do you think the woman being injected by the new small pox cure is worrying about? Write your answer in the box below.

Sickly smallpox – letter

☞ Pretend that you saw Edward Jenner give James Phipps the first ever smallpox vaccination. In the writing frame below, complete a letter that you will send to your friend explaining what you saw and why Edward Jenner did it.

Dear Mr Gaskell

    I saw something amazing today. A doctor called Edward Jenner_____

_____

_____

_____

_____

_____

_____

_____

_____

_____

_____

_____

_____

Yours sincerely

Miss D. Smith

Assessment sheet – Medical conditions

✓ Tick the boxes to show what you know.

I know:	Yes	Not sure	Don't know
what medicine was like before the nineteenth century			
the three different types of doctor			
who Edward Jenner was			
what smallpox vaccination means			
how medicine helped change people's lives			
how to use pictures as sources			
how to write a historical letter			

One thing that I remember the most about this unit is:

_____

_____

_____

_____

_____

King Cholera

Objectives

- Learn how outbreaks of cholera encouraged the improvement of sanitation
- Discover what the symptoms of cholera were
- Learn how to use a bar chart for historical information

Prior knowledge

Students need to be aware that medical improvements came about from sanitation improvements.

QCA link

Unit 11 Industrial changes action and reaction

NC links

History skills 2e, 3a

Scottish attainment targets

Environmental Studies – Society – People in the past Strand – Change and continuity, cause and effect Level D

Background

The main reason sanitation improved during the Industrial Revolution was the constant outbreaks of cholera. Scientists and doctors, such as Louis Pasteur and Robert Koch, discovered germs and were able to use this information to improve Britain's sanitation and, consequently, more people were able to live healthier lives.

Starter activity

Present students with the activity sheet 'King Cholera kills' and allow them two minutes to study the picture and try to remember its details. Students must then turn the picture over and give feedback to the teacher or write down the details that they can remember from the picture. This is a good activity for focusing pupils' attention on pictorial sources that contain lots of detail.

Resource sheet and activity sheets

'Edwin Chadwick' – read through the information and pay particular attention to the use of a chart to provide historical information.

Read through the Cholera poster in 'Cholera introduction' and then ask the students to complete the tasks based on the poster.

Ask the students to read through the information about cholera – causes and cures – in the 'Cholera facts' activity sheet and then complete the cloze sentence task.

'Cholera medicine poster' explains about medical tonics and gives information about effective adverts. Ask the students to draw an effective poster for a new cholera tonic.

Assessment sheet

Ask students to complete this sheet to evaluate their overall understanding of the effects of cholera during the Industrial Revolution and of the key skills developed.

Plenary

Lead a game of keyword hangman on the board to encourage students to use the new words from this topic.

King Cholera kills

Based on the cartoon 'Death's Dispensary' published in 1860.

☞ In pairs, examine the picture above and try to work out what the artist wants you to think.

Cholera introduction

Cholera Districts

The first symptom of cholera is <u>going to the toilet too often</u>.

When you feel _cramps in your legs, arms and stomach_ and no doctor is around then you can take the following medicine: _three teaspoonfuls of mustard powder in warm water_. You can also _drink salt in warm water_. These will make you vomit the cholera out of your body. You should also _put hot plates on your stomach_.

Try not to sit in a room with an infected person. You could catch the disease as well.

☞   Use the poster above to answer the questions below.

1.   What were the two symptoms of cholera?

    a) _____

    b) _____

2.   How could you cure cholera? (There are three ways.)

    a) _____

    b) _____

    c) _____

Cholera facts

The first time that somebody became sick from cholera was in 1831. It frightened the Victorians because people became sick very quickly. It also made both rich and poor people sick. More poor people became sick because they lived in bad housing and had bad food. During the Industrial Revolution, more than 100 000 people died from cholera.

What caused cholera?

People's toilets emptied into local rivers and streams. This polluted the water and made cholera. Doctors at the time did not know that this was what caused cholera. They said it was caused by bad air from rubbish left in the street.

Cures for cholera

1. Many cures for cholera did not work.
2. Some doctors told patients to wrap a wet towel around their waist.
3. Some doctors told patients to stay indoors and not eat fresh fruit.
4. Some doctors sold medicine that did not work.
5. After 1830, doctors saw that more people died in towns from cholera than in the countryside. They wanted to know why.

☞ Complete the passage below using the words from the wordbank to fill in the blank spaces.

The first victim of cholera was in _____. Both rich and _____ people could catch cholera. People became sick because their water was _____. There were lots of cures for _____ but they did not work. Doctors noticed that more people died in towns than the _____.

Wordbank				
countryside	cholera	polluted	poor	1831

Cholera medicine poster

☞ Design a poster for a new cholera medicine in the box below. Use the notes below to help you.

- Draw a medicine bottle and give it a good name – for example Cholera Cure or Medical Miracle.

- Say how much it costs – remember adverts have to tell you how much things cost.

- Say what it cures – list some of the symptoms and how useful the cure could be.

- Say how successful it is – remember you have to make people believe it will work.

Edwin Chadwick

A man called Edwin Chadwick was very worried about cholera. He agreed that it was bad air that was making people sick. Edwin Chadwick wanted to make towns cleaner so that people would be healthier.

Edwin Chadwick looked at Britain very closely and decided on three main things.

1.   More people died from disease than in wars.
2.   Parliament needed to pass laws to make Britain cleaner.
3.   People should pay to make Britain cleaner.

He looked at evidence that proved that people who lived in towns and worked in factories during the Industrial Revolution died younger. Look at the chart below to see the difference between towns and the countryside.

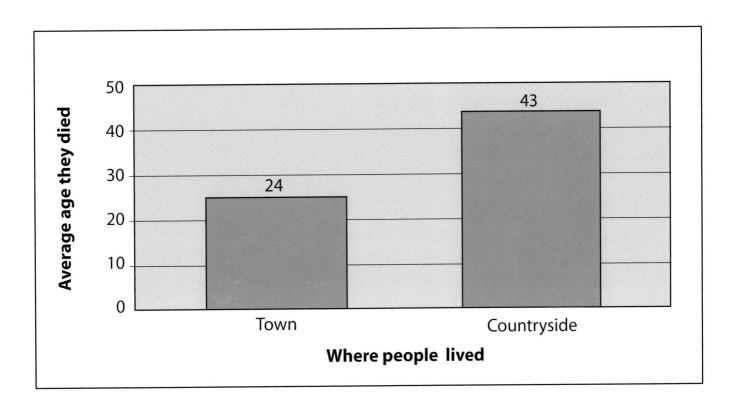

Assessment sheet – King Cholera

Use this sheet to see how much you can remember about cholera in Britain during the Industrial Revolution.

| ✓ | Tick the sentences below that are true. |

| X | Put a cross next to the sentences that are false. |

Cholera was a disease that only affected the poor.	
Pollution in drinking water caused cholera.	
All cures for cholera worked.	
More people died from cholera in the countryside.	
Edwin Chadwick did not care about cholera.	
Edwin Chadwick believed that bad air caused cholera.	
Edwin Chadwick discovered three main things about cholera.	
The average age of death in towns was 100.	

Specials! History Industrial Britain 1750–1900   © Folens (copiable page)

Teacher's notes

Queen Victoria

Objectives

- Learn about key figures at the end of the Industrial Revolution
- Understand the importance of the Queen to the reputation and image of Britain during the late nineteenth century
- Be able to accurately complete a timeline on a person

Prior knowledge

Students need to be aware that Queen Victoria was very important to Britain during the late nineteenth century.

QCA link

Unit 11 Industrial changes action and reaction

NC links

History skills 1, 7a

Scottish attainment targets

Environmental Studies – Society – People in the past
Strand – Time and historical sequence
Level C

Strand – People, events and societies of significance in the past
Level D

Background

Queen Victoria and Prince Albert were popular and powerful monarchs during the latter half of the Industrial Revolution. They encouraged economic growth and were proud of Britain's achievements, as demonstrated by the 1851 Great Exhibition held in London.

Starter activity

Provide students with a picture of Queen Victoria and ask them to evaluate what they think her personality might have been like.

Resource sheet and activity sheets

'Queen Victoria's life and reign' is a simple information sheet giving details about her reign and her family. Read through the sheet with the students. Emphasise the keywords and encourage students to fill in the definitions themselves.

'Queen Victoria timeline' provides a chronology and ranking activity that relies on information provided by the resource sheet 'Queen Victoria's life and reign'.

Assessment sheet

Ask students to complete this sheet to evaluate their knowledge about Queen Victoria and the Industrial Revolution.

Plenary

What can you remember? Students review/write down the main points learnt in the last lesson(s). This can be done in pairs or groups.

Queen Victoria's life and reign

Keywords
queen _____
parliament _____
empire _____
mourning _____
republic _____
monarch _____

What kind of a queen was Victoria?

Victoria was queen of England for a big part of the Industrial Revolution. She became **queen** in **1837**.

A queen is somebody who is the head of the country and helps **parliament** to control the country.

Victoria married Prince Albert of Saxe-Coburg in **1840**. Over the next eighteen years they had nine children.

Victoria was a popular queen and people liked her and Prince Albert.

Victoria and Albert made Britain very strong. They encouraged people to build factories and make lots of money for the **Empire**. It was Prince Albert who came up with the idea for the 'Great Exhibition'.

Prince Albert died from a disease called typhoid in **1861**. Queen Victoria wore black to show people that she was upset. After Prince Albert died, Queen Victoria spent a lot of time at her castle in Scotland. Some people were not happy and wanted Queen Victoria to stop being queen. They suggested that Britain could be a **republic**. This is a country without a **monarch**. She died on the Isle of Wight on 22 January **1901**.

Queen Victoria timeline

☞ Read the information about Queen Victoria on resource sheet 'Queen Victoria's life and reign' again.

1. Below is a timeline of events about things that happened during her reign. Complete the timeline to the best of your ability.

> **1837** > _____

> **1840** > _____

> **1861** > _____

> **1901** > _____

2. Using the information on the resource sheet 'Queen Victoria's life and reign', choose two reasons why you think that Queen Victoria and Prince Albert were popular in Great Britain.

a) _____

_____

b) _____

_____

Assessment sheet – Queen Victoria

Use this sheet to see how much you can remember about Queen Victoria.

| ✓ | Tick the sentences below that are true. |

| X | Put a cross next to the sentences that are false. |

Queen Victoria became queen in 2001.	

Queen Victoria married Prince Albert.	

Queen Victoria and Prince Albert had 21 children.	

People hated Queen Victoria and Prince Albert.	

After Albert died, Victoria spent a lot of time in Scotland.	

People in Britain wanted a republic.	

Queen Victoria died on the Isle of Wight.	

Queen Victoria died in 1952.	

Specials! History Industrial Britain 1750–1900   © Folens (copiable page)